Spiders in the Garden

DR ROD PRESTON-MAFHAM

Osmia Publications Limited

First published in 2003 by Osmia Publications Limited, Rothley, UK

©Osmia Publications 2003
©Rod and Ken Preston-Mafham (Text) 2003
©Rod and Ken Preston-Mafham (Photographs) 2003

The authors hereby assert their moral right to be identified as the authors of this work and the publisher undertakes to observe such assertion and to impose the same conditions on its licences.

ISBN 1-904770-03-7

A CIP record for this title is available from the British Library.

Cover photograph: Pisaura mirabilis Wedding present or nusery tent spider (Pisaurdae) male ©Ken Preston-Mafham Premaphotos Wildlife

Design by New Leaf, Loughborough

Printed and bound in Thailand by Gift Export Co., Ltd

About the author

Having trained as a zoologist the author spent the first 20 years of his working life teaching biology. It was at this time that he developed his interest in spiders, partly as a result of he and his brother being commissioned to write 'Spiders of the World' for Blandford Press. Since then he has either authored or co-authored further books on the subject of spiders. He presently lives with his wife Jean and daughter Lauren, (his older son and daughter are married and have left home), in Bodmin in Cornwall, his large, partly wild garden holding most of the spider species mentioned in this volume. As well as being a prolific writer on wildlife subjects he and his wife and brother run the wildlife picture library, Premaphotos Wildlife.

I'm told that the spider

Has coiled up inside her

Enough silky material

To spin an aerial

One-way track

To the moon and back

Whilst I

Cannot even catch a fly

ANONYMOUS

Contents

The colour plates

Introduction to spiders 1

No matter where you live, be it in the depths of the country, in the suburbs, in a town or city or, even if you only have window boxes, you will find that they will provide a home for spiders of one kind or another. Obviously, the greater the variety of habitats in your garden, the greater the variety of spider species that you are likely to encounter.

To increase the scope of this book the concept of the garden is quite broad in that it encompasses any part of your property outside the house. This includes the house wall, window frames, roof and any other attached structures, as long as they are outside. In the garden itself you can include greenhouses, sheds, summerhouses, gazebos and any similar structures, for as far as the spiders are concerned these are just 'caves' or represent overhanging banks, favourite homes for many spider species.

Male and female spiders tend to lead different lives. Of the web-building species, the females spend all of their time in the web, catching prey, growing to maturity and then continuing to feed until their body is swollen with eggs. The smaller males require less food and, once they are mature, spend a lot of their time searching for mates. Thus it is in webs you are most likely to find female spiders. Throughout the text on web-builders, therefore, I will tend to talk about 'she' when discussing the activities that go on in relation to the web.

Of the active hunters, which do not make permanent webs, one is just as likely to come across males as females.

WHAT IS A SPIDER?

Most of us will recognise a spider when we see one, because nearly every householder in the British Isles has to tolerate the house spider, which so often ends up in the bath. Also, most of us will have, at one time or another, watched some of the marvellous documentaries on spiders, which have been shown on television.

We all know that spiders differ from insects in the number of legs that they have, spiders having 4 pairs and insects just 3 pairs. Also, while insects have the body divided into a separate head, thorax and abdomen, the spider head and thorax form a single structure, the cephalothorax, attached to the abdomen by a fairly narrow waist. The top of the cephalothorax is covered by a protective plate called the carapace. The other main difference, of course, is that spiders never have wings, unlike insects, which usually do.

Our spiders vary a great deal in size, so in order to help recognise them the length of the body, from the front of the head to the tip of the abdomen is given for each species discussed. Males are usually smaller than females, so the shortest length given is that of the smallest males while the longest length is that of the largest females.

WHAT LOOKS LIKE A SPIDER BUT IS NOT?

The spiders are members of a large group of animals called the Arachnida. In common with the spiders, arachnids have 4 pairs of legs and also include the scorpions, the two types of whip scorpions, the sun spiders, the harvestmen and the mites and ticks. Most of these are not found in this country, though one or two species of scorpion have established small colonies in the southeast of England. You will, however, come across two of these other types of arachnid in the garden, the harvestmen and the mites. You might also come across ticks, on your pet dog or cat, especially if they have been wandering around near sheep or hedgehogs.

Harvestmen are most like spiders but they usually have very long legs in relation to the size of the body and close examination will reveal that the head, thorax and abdomen all form a single, usually rather globular, structure. They are most often seen wandering over the house wall or climbing over vegetation in search of prey, which consists mainly of small insects.

© Dr Rod Preston-Mafham, Premaphotos Wildlife.

Dicranopalpus ramosus Splay-legged harvestman (Opiliones: phlalangidae) walking across a leaf having shed one of its legs.

Most mites are very tiny, have very short legs, no separate divisions of the body and, at least those found in the garden, are usually red. The biggest of them, the earth mites, may reach 2 or 3mm in length. They have a very furry body, are deep pink in colour and, as their name implies, are usually to be found wandering over the soil. Most often encountered, however, are much smaller species, no more than a millimetre long, which often gather in huge numbers on fences and vegetation. These again are deep pink in colour but should not be confused with that awful pest, the red spider mite, which is in fact yellow, tiny and is usually found in the greenhouse on a variety of cultivated plants.

SPIDERS AND SILK

A common ability of males and females of all spiders is to produce silk. This substance is very important to them and it is used in a number of different ways, more of which later. The silk itself is produced in glands in the spider's abdomen and, since there are several different kinds of silk, there are different kinds of gland to produce it. The silk is produced as a liquid, which is squeezed out through nozzles on the spinnerets, of which our spiders normally have 3 pairs at the end of the abdomen. Different types of nozzle, or spigot as they are correctly termed, occur for each type of silk. As the fine stream of liquid hits the air it reacts with oxygen to form the strands of silk as we know it. As the silk is extruded, the spider pulls on it, the harder the pull, the stronger the silk. This silk is extremely strong, some types being stronger than steel threads of the same diameter. It is also very resistant to bacterial action, which accounts for the fact that cobwebs hang around often months or even years after the spider that made it has died or moved on.

It is well known that the silk is used to make the familiar web, which the spider uses to trap prey, but silk also has other uses. It forms a waterproof lining in the burrow of those spiders that live below ground, it is used to form a protective cocoon around the spider's eggs and it is used to wrap up prey to prevent it from struggling and escaping from the spider's clutches. Less obvious than this is the fact that when wandrering around in search of prey, rather than using a web, many spiders leave a strand of silk behind them. When off the ground, this gives the spider a means of escape from attackers: by letting go of its perch, it drops down to safety on the silken line. Even web-builders will drop down from their webs on one of these safety lines if molested.

The females of species which do not have permanent webs coat their silk with pheromones, chemical signals, which attract males, who follow the trail of silk to find a mate.

HOW SPIDERS FEED

All spiders are predators, feeding mainly on insects but also taking other small arthropods. A few, including some British species, feed on other spiders. More detail of precisely how the different types of spiders catch their prey will be given in later chapters.

With few exceptions spiders immobilise and kill their prey by injecting them with poison. The poison comes from glands in the head and is injected through the needle-sharp, hollow fangs, which are on the front of the spider's head. Once the prey is dead, it may be dealt with in one of two ways. Some species bite holes and pour digestive enzymes from the mouth into the prey's body. This turns the prey's body contents into a soup, which the spider then sucks up. When the meal is finished the spider just drops the empty husk to the ground.

Other species of spider chew the prey, a little at a time, pouring enzymes on to it as it does so. As the body is digested, so the resulting liquid is sucked up. At the end, all that is left of the prey is an unrecognisable mass of indigestible body parts.

AN UNUSUAL WAY OF MATING

Spiders have a most unusual way of mating. On either side of the head is a short, jointed appendage, a sort of feeler, called the palp, which is used for tasting food. This is its sole function in females, but in males it has a second role. The end segment is highly modified to form what, in simple terms, might be described as a bulb pipette, just like the one used for picking up and administering eye-drops. The male releases a drop of semen from the reproductive opening on his abdomen and sucks it up into the reservoir in each palp. During mating he places the end of each palp into the female's reproductive opening, on the underside of the abdomen, and then squeezes the semen into her. The process is actually fraught with danger for the male, for he is normally smaller than his mate, and if he does not go through the correct approach to her during courtship, he can end up getting eaten, though this appears, from my experience, to be a relatively rare event.

HANDLING SPIDERS

Despite the fact that they are killers, spiders are in fact very delicate creatures and need to be handled very carefully if they are not to be fatally damaged. Unlike many insects, you cannot pick them up in a pair of light forceps, for the abdomen is particularly tender and will break open with even the gentlest of squeezes. The best way to catch spiders is in a small glass specimen tube or, for the bigger species, a specimen pot, i.e., the ones used by the medical profession for collecting urine samples. Otherwise any small glass or plastic jar will suffice. Details of most of the bigger spiders will then be seen with a good hand lens, though for the smaller species a binocular microscope will be useful. When you have finished with them put them back where you found them.

Lace-weavers 2

No, this is nothing to do with using silk and bobbins to produce lace but refers to a family of spiders which uses silk in rather a different way from the majority of spiders. As well as having spinnerets, which produce strands of silk in the normal way, these spiders, produce a special silk, which has a lacy appearance and which gives them their common name.

On the underside of these spiders, in front of the spinnerets, is a special plate, called a cribellum, through which pass large numbers of tiny holes. Towards the end of each of the hind pair of legs is a row of thick hairs, which form a comb, the calamistrum, not dissimilar to the one with which we comb our hair. Production of silk in these spiders is a bit more complicated than in other families. The spider produces two straight strands of silk from the front pair of spinnerets and at the same time a second pair of strands from the posterior pair of spinnerets. Leaving the front pair of strands untouched, the spider uses the combs on its hind legs to pull the posterior silk strands out into a series of loops. Simultaneously, a sticky, bluish secretion from the cribellum is attached to the looped threads producing what is referred to as 'hackled band silk'.

Four different families of our spiders make this kind of silk but only one family has members that are commonly found in gardens. These are the members of the Amaurobiidae. The common lace weaver, *Amaurobius similis*, which is 6-12mm in length, is most likely to be found making its lair in holes in walls or under stones. The strands of fluffy hackled band silk are quite easily recognised, since they are much thicker than the strands found in webs such as the orb web of the garden spider. The spider lays her silk in a haphazard manner over the area surrounding the entrance to her lair. Rather than building a new web every night, the spider adds a few lengths of fresh silk each evening. Its aim is to catch walking insect prey, whose claws and bristles become entangled in the fluffy silk. Its struggles soon attract the spider and she quickly bites it to immobilise it before dragging it into her lair in the wall. It is actually worth going out, just as it gets dark,

©Ken Preston-Mafham, Premaphotos Wildlife.

Amaurobius similis Common lace weaver spider female (Amaurobiidae) extruding hackled-band silk through her cribellum and combing it out with the calmistrum on her hind leg.

to watch one of these spiders laying down her hackled band. She will usually tolerate the light of a torch just long enough for you to get an idea of how she produces this very elaborate silk.

Rather similar in appearance to but slightly smaller, (4-9mm), than the common lace weaver is the window lace weaver, *Amaurobius fenestralis*. Look for her web on the walls of the house, especially around window frames and extending across the glass, but also under any loose bark on trees in the garden. The largest member of the family is the black lace weaver, *Amaurobius ferox*, (8-15mm), which is less common than the other two species and is best sought beneath stones and logs. It is strictly speaking not black but very dark brown, with paler markings on the abdomen, the other two species being more of a medium brown, again with paler markings.

The female spider lays her eggs within her lair, covering them over with a thick layer of silk to protect them. She then stands on guard over them until they hatch out. In my garden in Cornwall, females may produce more than one brood, but in colder areas just a single batch of eggs is laid. The female remains with her young after they have hatched but eventually, having completed her life's work, she dies. Her emaciated body is not wasted, however, for it then provides a meal for her offspring before they eventually disperse to find suitable lairs of their own.

While the common and window lace weavers are found across most of the British Isles the black lace weaver is uncommon in Scotland and in Ireland is found mainly in the southern half.

Woodlouse spiders and their kin 2

There are two species of woodlouse spider, both very similar in appearance, their differences only being easily visible under the microscope. *Dysdera crocata*, at 9-15mm is a bigger spider than *D. erythrina* (7 – 10mm). The woodlouse spiders are easy to recognise for the carapace and legs are deep reddish in colour while the rather tubular abdomen is dirty white to fawn. The most noticeable thing about them is their jaws, which are huge, the fangs being nearly as long as the carapace. The reason for this lies in the fact, as you may have guessed from their name, that they both feed on woodlice. Woodlice are quite well protected with tough plates forming a kind of body armour. In order to feed on a woodlouse the spider opens its jaws wide, places one fang on the top of the prey and the other beneath it and then closes the jaws, just like a pair of pincers.

Both species are most often found under stones and slabs in gardens, especially if it is slightly damp beneath them and they warm up in the sun, conditions which are also just right for woodlice. They remain under the stones during the day, hunting taking place during the hours of darkness. Of the two species, *Dysdera crocata* is the most common, though it only just gets into Scotland, is found mainly in North Wales and has a patchy, but mainly southern, distribution in Ireland. *D. erythrina* is much more southern, being absent from Scotland and Northern England, occurring in South Wales only and just a few counties in Ireland.

Closely related to the woodlouse spiders is the snake-back spider, sometimes called the leopard spider, *Segestria senoculata*. The body shape of this spider is rather tubular. The carapace is dark, almost black, while the abdomen is grey with a set of triangular marks down the centre, a bit like those of some types of snake, hence it common name; some individuals, however, have the marks are joined up to form a continuous dark line. The legs, in contrast, are pale brown, with a few darker marking on them.

The best place to look for this spider, which ranges from 6 to 10mm in length, is in small gaps in woodwork or between window frames and the house wall. Look for a tubular web with a network of single lines radiating out from it onto the surrounding surfaces, just like the spokes of a wheel. The snake-back spider sits in her tubular lair and, should a passing insect happen to walk over and touch one of the trip-lines, she will rush out and grab it.

The snake-back spider is very common with a broad distribution and is found almost everywhere, the exceptions being Orkney and Shetland. If, however, you live in certain south coast towns you may be lucky enough to have in your garden or house walls the big cousin of the snake-back spider, *Segestria florentina*. The female is a big spider, up to 22mm long, dark brown in colour with similar abdominal markings to *S. senoculata*. Again, she lives in a tubular lair in a hole in the wall. Touch one of her trip wires with a piece of grass and she will dart out, flashing her huge, greenish jaws as she does so. She really is something to look out for.

©Ken Preston-Mafham, Premaphotos Wildlife

Dysdera crocata Woodlouse spider female (Dysderidae)

Crab spiders 4

The crab spiders are well-named for not only do they have rather flattened bodies, like crabs, but they also tend to walk in a similar scuttling manner. The most noticeable thing about crab spiders in general is that the first two pairs of legs are longer and more powerfully built than the other two pairs. Although variable in shape, the carapace is usually at least as wide as it is long and the same is true of the abdomen. These spiders are sit-and-wait hunters, spending their lives perched on vegetation, some species on the ground, waiting for passing prey. They sit with their front legs apart and as soon as an insect comes in reach, it is grasped, pulled into contact with the jaws and the fatal bite is administered. They seem to have a very powerful poison, for the prey is usually immobilised almost instantaneously.

The crab spider most likely to encountered in the average garden is the small, brown species, *Xysticus cristatus*, which is found just about everywhere, including Orkney and Shetland. While females can reach 8mm in length the males are only ever just over half this size. Although their overall colour is brown, they do have lighter and darker patterns on both the carapace and abdomen. Most often found on garden plants of all kinds, this little crab spider will also hunt on the ground.

If you are very lucky you might come across a pair who are about to mate, for the process is quite unusual. On finding a female the male approaches her boldly and climbs onto her back. He then appears to walk around all over her but in reality he is weaving a network of silk over her body and is tying her down with it to the leaf or whatever they are standing on. Once she is 'tied up', the male then mates with her, a procedure which takes an hour or more. He then walks off, leaving her to disentangle herself from her bonds. It is assumed that this ritual prevents the female from attacking the male while he positions himself to mate with her.

Those of you who live in the southern half of both England and Ireland, or in the Welsh

©Ken Preston-Mafham. Premaphotos Wildlife.

Misumena vatia Flower spider female (Thomisidae) in ambush pose on a moon daisy

border counties, especially in rural areas, are likely to come across a larger and more attractive crab spider, the common flower spider, *Misumena vatia*. She may reach 11mm in length but the male is tiny, reaching just 4mm. The common flower spider is off-white in colour, with greenish marks on the carapace and usually, though not always, a deep pink stripe down either side of the abdomen. The male, however, has a dark brown carapace and front 2 pairs of legs and a white abdomen with dark stripes on it. She likes to sit in flowers because these are regularly visited by suitable prey. Normally she takes anything from house fly size upwards, including honey and bumble bees, and she ignores anything smaller as not making a worthwhile meal. She always sits absolutely motionless in wait for prey, for any movement would betray her position to passing birds, who would find her a tasty snack.

Sometimes you may come across a bright yellow spider of similar size and appearance to the common flower spider. Do not be fooled into thinking that you have found another species, for *Misumena vatia* has the ability to change its colour from white to yellow, and back again, at will. Quite why it does so, the process taking 2 to 3 days, no one is absolutely sure. The yellow spiders are often found sitting in the yellow centre of flowers such as the ox-eye daisy, but then again I have found them sitting equally happily in the centre of blue flowers, where to the human eye, at least, they are most conspicuous.

Jumping spiders 5

It may seem strange to use such a word to describe any kind of creepy-crawly but the jumping spiders can truly be called 'endearing'. This is because many species appear to interact with us when we are observing them closely, for reasons which will soon become apparent.

Although many tropical jumping spiders can be brilliantly coloured and can exceed 20mm in length most of our species are less than 10mm long and are usually rather drab. The jumping spiders are active hunters, wandering around on vegetation, the ground, on rocks and buildings in search of prey, which the pick up and home in on with their very keen eyesight. Their eyes are arranged in a particular pattern, which gives them this acute vision. The front of the face is rather flat and bears two pairs of forward-pointing eyes, a large central pair and a somewhat smaller outer pair. A further two pairs of eyes are situated on the top of the head region of the carapace. To see how these eyes work let's look for one of the common jumping spiders of house and garden, the zebra spider, *Salticus scenicus*.

As its name indicates, the zebra spider is mainly black and white, with noticeable striping on the abdomen. Females grow to around 7mm long, males are smaller, up to 6mm long, but this includes around 2mm forwards extension of their rather large jaws. They are most often found, moving in fits and starts, on the wall of the house or shed, sometimes ending up indoors via an open window. Although they are in search of insect prey, they do in fact take notice of us. As we approach, they first pick us up through the eyes on top of the head, which detect direction of movement but do not form a clear image. They then swivel round in the direction of the movement and look directly at us with the huge eyes on the front of the head. These eyes are large enough to be seen with our naked eyes, the overall appearance of its face being somewhat like that of a monkey, which makes it rather endearing. To get a closer look at this spider slowly stretch a finger towards it; the likelihood is that it will leap on to it and you can then examine it at your leisure. Notice

Salticus scenicus Zebra spider (Jumping spider - Salticidae) on a cactus in a greenhouse

that, as it leaps it lets out a silk thread behind it, so that if it misses its aim, which it seldom does, it can climb back up the line to its original position. Had there been a small insect on the tip of your finger, then the zebra spider would have had it. It is, of course, the large eyes which are used to produce what is believed to be a fairly sharp image of the prey and, with binocular vision, how far away, it is. Most species, including the zebra spider, get to within two or three body lengths of their prey before pouncing, but some species can jump more than 20 times their own body length. The zebra spider occurs of most of England and Wales, the southern half of Scotland as well as the southern half and the northeast corner of Ireland.

While the zebra spider is the most commonly encountered of our jumping spiders there are others, which are often found in gardens. Most obvious are the two species of *Heliophanus*. Both species are all black in colour and the females, which have pale yellow legs, reach around 6mm in length. The males, which have darker legs, are shining black and are usually to be seen rushing around on the ground or on vegetation in search of females. Both species of spider are found over most of England and Wales but they have a very patchy distribution in Ireland and Scotland, where they are absent from the far north and most of the islands.

Wolf spiders 6

The common name of wolf spider for the family Lycosidae is not strictly accurate. Wolves hunt in packs and although wolf spiders may often be seen together in quite large numbers, they all act as individuals, not helping one another out as wolves do.

The wolf spiders most often found in gardens are members of the genus *Pardosa*, there being 15 different species in the British Isles, some of which are rare and with a very limited distribution. Most species are ground dwellers or at the most climb on to low vegetation. Unlike wolves, they do not chase around after prey but wait for it to pass by. They have a pair of large eyes on the front of the head, which enables them to get a sight on the prey before they rush at it and deliver the fatal bite.

The species most likely to be encountered in gardens are the spotted wolf spider, *Pardosa amentata*, and *P. pullata*, which have a very wide distribution in these islands, one or other of them being found just about everywhere. They are best sought on sunny days in summer when they will be found sitting around on logs, stones, bare patches of earth or amongst grass, sunning themselves. They are not easily told apart without microsopic examination, though *P. pullata* tends to be darker brown then *P. amentata*. *P. pullata* is the wolf spider most likely to be found in cities but it also survives on mountains up to around 2000 feet.

The *Pardosa* wolf spiders spend the winter in an immature state, reappearing the following spring to begin feeding again and to moult to adulthood in April or May. One favourite overwintering site in the garden is the greenhouse and as a result you may find them active on warm winter days. Once they are adult it is worthwhile watching out for their courtship, which is often carried out on a log or stone in direct sunlight. The smaller males approach the females and signal to them with their palps, each species having a different pattern of signals to avoid cross-mating between them. If she is in a receptive mood the female will allow the male to approach and mate with her, otherwise she will rebuff him, often by just

Pardosa amentata Spotted wolf spider female (Lycosidae) carrying her egg sac

running away. Amazingly, the male will often sit and signal with his palps to the place where the female was originally perched. It is presumed that she has left her sexual scents, her pheromones, there and he is still reacting to these.

Having mated, female wolf spiders, lay their eggs in a silken egg-sac. She then anchors the egg-sac to her spinnerets and carries it around with her until they are ready to hatch. She is somehow able to detect when this moment arrives, for she cuts a hole in the egg-sac to allow her offspring to emerge. They are unable to do this on their own. They do not now rush off to lead independent lives but instead they climb onto her back and remain with her for several days while she carries them around with her. Should one fall off it will immediately rush back to her, following the silken lifeline that dragged out behind it as it fell. Only after moulting their skin for the first time do they leave her. Female wolf spiders with young are easily recognisable: they look as if their abdomen is covered in a layer of fur.

THE WEDDING PRESENT SPIDER

Members of the family Pisauridae are also sometimes called wolf spiders, because the habits of at least some them are very similar to those of the lycosid wolf spiders just described. The Pisauridae includes the fishing spiders, which hunt on the surface of ponds, catching drowning insects and also tadpoles and small fish, which come to the surface. On land we find the nursery tent spiders, whose females construct a silken tent in which their eggs hatch and their young remain until they are ready to go off on their own.

Our nursery tent spider, *Pisaura mirabilis,* has a very special behaviour and is now often referred to as the wedding present spider. It is quite a large spider, the females reaching 15mm in length, with long legs and is handsomely marked in various shades of brown, with yellowish patches. She is most likely to be found in suburban or country gardens, where her favourite habitat is nettle beds, though she will also be found sitting around on almost any low vegetation.

Before he can mate the male must find a 'wedding present' for his prospective bride, this usually taking the form of a juicy fly. Having caught a fly, the male now wraps it neatly in a layer of silk and goes off in search of a mate, who often as not he will find sunning herself on a large leaf. He approaches her carefully, for she is larger than he is, holding the fly out in front of him. If she is ready to accept him she approaches him and grasps the fly in her jaws. The male now mates with her, a process which can take more than an hour, while she feeds happily on her 'wedding present'.

The female wedding present spider then lays her eggs, wrapping them in layers of silk to form a large ball, which she then carries around in her jaws. She very cleverly keeps them at the right sort of temperature for development, shading them from the sun if it is hot, sitting in the sun and warming them if the weather has previously been cool and damp. On detecting that the eggs are about to hatch, she attaches the sac to some suitable vegetation, loosens the covering so that the young can escape, and then constructs the silken tent around them. She usually then sits close to the tent for the few days that the young remain there. Eventually, they moult their skin and then leave home, the last their mother will see of them.

Pisaura mirabilis Wedding present spider female (Pisauridae) basking

©Ken Preston-Mafham, Premaphotos Wildlife.

Pisaura mirabilis is common in England and Wales, but in Scotland is absent from most southern counties, being found in much of the highlands; it is absent from the far north and the islands and is found only in the southern half of Ireland. The best way of finding this species is to look out for the tent containing spiderlings.

Sheet web spiders 7

This is the family of spiders that contains that well-known frightener of householders, the house spider, which so often falls into the bath as it wanders around our homes. There are, in fact, a number of species of *Tegenaria* to which the name house spider can be applied and only one of these is almost always found inside houses and seldom outside. Some of our Tegenarias are quite happy to spend the cold months of winter inside our homes, leaving them when it warms up in spring, while others spend all of their lives outside.

The largest of the house spiders is *Tegenaria duellica*, a darkish, rather hairy species whose females reach up to 22mm in length. They build their sheet webs leading out from the funnel-shaped lair in the corners of rooms, in garages, sheds and other outhouses and also in suitable nooks and crannies outside in the garden. The sheet web acts as a trap for insects that end up walking over it, the spider rushing out from her lair to grab it. This species is widespread over much of the British Isles.

If you have a large garden with plenty of trees you may find a much smaller species, only one third of the size of the previous one, and this is *T. silvestris*. This likes to build its webs under logs, stones, bark and other similar places. This species has a limited distribution in England and Wales.

The yard spider, *T. agrestis*, has been increasing its range in the UK from a previously southern distribution. It again resembles *T. duellica* but is intermediate in size between that species and *T. silvestris*. It should be sought under sheets of wood or corrugated iron, which have been left lying around the garden. It is said to be quite an aggressive spider, biting if handled carelessly but causing no harm.

Tegenaria agrestis Yard spider male (Agelenidae)

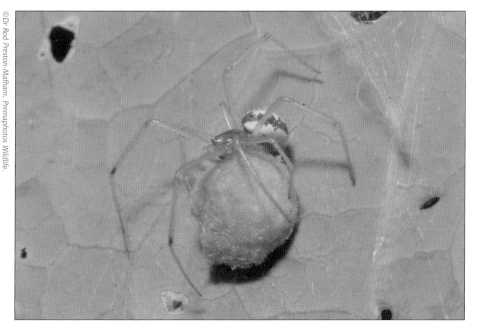

Enoplognatha ovata Red and white spider (Theridiidae) guarding her egg sac

Comb-footed spiders 8

This family contains a number of common garden spiders. The abdomen, especially that of the female, is clearly globular and the family includes the notorious black widow spiders. Thankfully none occur in the British Isles, though one is found in Europe. The name comb-footed derives from the fact that there is a row of curved, serrated bristles on the hind legs, which the spider uses to throw strands of silk over the prey in order to subdue it. These spiders construct a scaffold web, consisting of vertical and horizontal lines arranged in a seemingly haphazard manner. A number of the vertical lines are sticky and, in those species which build above the ground, are aimed at catching flying insects as they blunder through the scaffolding. Others live at ground level and have sticky vertical lines attached to the ground, aimed this time at catching insects as they walk through the web.

The most easily recognised, and probably the commonest, of the garden comb-footed spiders is the red-and-white cobweb weaver, *Enoplognatha ovata*. This is not a big spider, being just 6mm long when fully grown and has three distinct colour forms. The basic colour is a sort of yellowish off-white and this is how some forms appear. In addition to this base colour, some individuals have a deep pink line running down either side of the abdomen. In some forms, however, the upper side of the abdomen is entirely deep pink and the rest of the spider is off-white. Females can normally be found in webs on low plants or, once mated, sitting with their bluish egg-sac in curled leaves. I have even found one like this in a curled cabbage leaf.

This spider has a very wide distribution in the British Isles, being absent from just a few counties in Ireland as well as the Outer Hebrides and Orkney. It is, however, found in Shetland.

Search the greenhouse, shed or any outhouse or, in warmer counties in the south, outside under stones etc., for the rabbit hutch spider, *Steatoda bipunctata*. This reaches about 7mm in length, has a very shiny abdomen, which can vary from light to dark brown and lives in a rather untidy scaffold web. Fairly common over most of England and east and north Wales, this species has a patchy distribution in Scotland and is very rare in Ireland. The closely related species, *Steatoda nobilis,* is quite a large spider, females reaching 14mm in length. This spider has become well established in southern English counties over the 100 or so years since it was introduced into the country from the Canary Islands and Madeira. Apart from its size it can be told apart from the rabbit hutch spider by the fact that the upper side of the abdomen is patterned rather than just comprising one colour. Although mainly a house-dweller it can live outside in the south and the reason for mentioning it here is that it does bite if it is roughly handled. It does not hurt much, the bite being described as similar to a very mild wasp sting.

Finally, we come to a very interesting little spider, which lives in my garden in the country but could occur in almost any garden, which is well stocked with bushes, though it seems to like gorse and holly bushes most of all. This is the mothercare spider, *Theridion sisyphium.* This, and a number of closely related species, which can also turn up in gardens, builds a scrappy scaffold web in a bush, usually towards the outer ends of the branches. Attached to the web is a silken lair, roughly in the shape of an inverted cone, in which she sits in wait for prey to get trapped. The lair often incorporates the remains of prey in its walls, much of which is also left lying around the rest of the web, the whole lot having a very messy appearance.

She is a prettily-marked little spider, little being the operative word, for she only reaches 4mm in length when fully grown. Her claim to fame is the way in which she cares for her young once they have hatched. Rather than leaving her straight away, they remain in her lair for the first few weeks of their lives. At first she feeds them with a sort of spider 'milk'. She hangs head down in her lair and releases a drop of nutritious fluid from her mouth from which the spiderlings then feed. As they get older they come to rely less on their mother but instead share the food that she catches in her web. They will even help their mother subdue it by throwing their own silk over it to add to that which she produces. The mothercare spider is found over almost the whole of the British Isles, though her distribution is patchy in the north of both Ireland and Scotland.

Orb weaving spiders 9

For many people the orb weavers, with their familiar circular webs, are the archetypal spiders and a good range of species is found in our gardens, wherever they may be. There are, in fact, two separate families of orb weaving spiders whose members you are likely to come across, the Tetragnathidae, which includes the big-jawed spiders, and the Araneidae, typified by the garden spider.

Let us first look at some members of the second of these families, the Araneidae. The garden, or cross, spider, *Araneus diadematus,* is a very familiar species found over virtually the whole of the British Isles. Fully grown it reaches around 13mm in length and is easily recognised by the white cross on the top of the abdomen, though this is occasionally absent in some specimens. The ground colour of the abdomen can be very variable, from very pale yellowish-fawn to a deep reddish-orange or from pale to dark brown. The female builds her web on suitable strong vegetation from around a foot to 10 feet or so above the ground. During the day you may find her sat, head down, in the centre of her web or just as likely in her lair, a silken tent beneath a leaf a short distance above or to the side of the web. From this you will see that a signal line runs to the web and she sits in her lair with at least one leg resting on it. Any struggling insect caught in the web send vibrations down the signal line and the spider will rush out immediately to investigate. Easily managed prey is immediately swathed in silk while a larger insect may be given a quick bite on the leg to subdue it before it, too, is wrapped up. If she is hungry, she will take the food straight to her lair to feed, otherwise she may leave it hanging in the web until she is ready for it.

Late in summer or in early autumn the female reaches maturity and is ready to mate. At this time you may find the much smaller male in or near the female's web as he tempts her into mating, a business which for him is fraught with danger. He has to persuade the large female of his good intentions and indicate to her that he is not just another hapless insect, which has blundered into her web. He does so by approaching her with slow, deliberate steps, sending her a regular signal of his approach by tweaking the web with his legs. He is not without a back-up line of defence, though, for he runs a lifeline out behind him and if she lunges at him, as she often does on his first approaches, he drops out of her web and away from her jaws. This series of events may be repeated many times until eventually he is permitted to mate with her. It has been reported that the male of this species usually gets eaten by the female following mating. In the many times, however, that I have observed courtship of this species in the wild I have never seen the male eaten. Furthermore, in observing hundreds of females in their webs I have only ever once come across the remains of a male who had served as a meal for his mate. Cannibalism may happen more often under laboratory conditions, but that is a different story altogether.

The female usually makes some attempt at hiding her egg-sac, which is easy to recognise for it is quite large and wrapped in yellow silk. It is from these that in the warmth of the spring sunshine the masses of little brown and yellow babies hatch. They remain close together in a ball for some days, scattering in all directions if disturbed. Once any possible danger has passed, however, they follow their lifelines back until they all come together again in their neat little ball.

©Ken Preston-Mafham, Premaphotos Wildlife.

Araneus diadematus Garden spider female (Araneidae) in her orb web

You will have to look into clusters of leaves on bushes and fruit trees to find our, the green orb weaver, *Araniella cucurbitina*. This pretty little spider is bright green, with a red spot on the underside of the abdomen. She builds her small, horizontal orb web between the leaves at the end of a twig or across the whole of a very large leaf or even a large flower. She reaches a maximum length of just 6mm and her prey is restricted to relatively small flying insects. You will find this spider over much of the British Isles, though it is missing from a number of counties in Ireland and Scotland.

The rather sinister looking spider, the walnut, or black, orb weaver *Nuctenea umbratica*, is to be found on houses and outbuildings as well as on trees. This species is pale through dark-brown to almost black. She has a leaf-shaped pattern on the top of the abdomen and reaches about the same size as the garden spider when fully grown but has a noticeably flattened body, allowing her to find a lair in cracks under loose bark or similar narrow spaces on the garden shed. During the day you will find the tattered remains of her orb web, which is made up of a very tough silk. She is, however, active during the hours of darkness, coming out at dusk to repair her web, which she uses to trap night-flying insects such as moths. She is fairly common over much of England, Wales and Scotland but is rare in Ireland.

Also on the house, outbuildings or on fences we find the rather oddly named 'missing sector orb weaver', *Zygiella x-notata*, so called because the web has a very distinctive, "incomplete" appearance, a number of spokes being absent. While her cephalothorax and legs are brown, the abdomen is silvery grey, with a brown leaf-shaped marking on the upper surface. Like many orb weavers, she rests in her lair with a leg on the signal line running down to the centre of the web. She is common over much of the British Isles.

The other common orb weaving spiders found in gardens belong to the family Tetragnathidae. The common orb weaver, *Meta segmentata*, and the very similar *Meta mengei* are very common, with a wide distribution in England, Wales and Scotland though they are less common in Ireland. Because they can only be distinguished under the microscope we will consider them together.

From my experience they tend to build their webs slightly lower down than those of the garden spider, with which they could be confused. Unlike the garden spider, however, they do not build a lair and they do not have a signal line running to a favourite perch and there is normally a noticeable empty space at the centre of the web. You will usually find the spider sitting at the centre of her web, where she can quite easily be identified by looking at the underside of her abdomen, which has a broad, dark stripe running down the centre, bordered by two paler bands. *M. segmentata* is a slightly bigger species, reaching 8mm in length, about 2mm more than the biggest females of *M. mengei*. Once the females have reached full size, you will often find that the web is occupied by another similar-looking spider with a smaller abdomen; this is the male. Sometimes you may even find two males in the web competing for the female's attention. Males usually wait until the female is engaged in having a meal, often as not a fly of some kind, before they attempt to mate with her.

The last of the orb weavers, are the long-jawed spiders, *Tetragnatha* species. The species likely to turn up in the garden are difficult for the beginner to tell apart, so we will just consider big-jawed spiders as a group. Their common name is very appropriate, for they do indeed have large jaws in relation to their size. They are very easily distinguished from other orb weavers, for they have a long, slim body and long legs. The large jaws, as well as being used to kill their prey, are also used in mating. Males and females meet face to face, locking their jaws together by means of various projections on them. This enables the male to mate in safety, as the female is unable to unlock her jaws and attack him. As soon as he has finished mating, he must unlock his jaws and drop away from her on his lifeline.

The long-jawed spiders make a relatively flimsy web, with no lair or signal line and, unlike other orb weavers, it is not usually vertical and at times is almost horizontal. The spider normally sits in the web but, if disturbed, it will run to the nearest blade of grass or stem and then stretch its legs out along it, pressing the body close to it so that it becomes well camouflaged from possible enemies. The only area of the whole of the British Isles from which the common species of long-jawed spiders are absent is the Shetlands.

Money spiders 10

The money spiders belong to the family Linyphiidae, which is the largest family in terms of numbers of species to be found in our islands. More than 270 species have been discovered here. Most are black or grey and are no more than 2-3mm long. Their name comes from the belief that, if one of them settles on you, you are going to come into money. To kill one is very unlucky!

Money spiders build a hammock-like web, with a tangle of scaffolding lines above and below it as supports. Flying insects collide with the scaffolding lines and tumble onto the sheet beneath, where the web's occupant lies in wait. As the insect struggles on the surface of the sheet the spider, which is on the underside, rushes out and bites it from below, through the silk. Once the insect has been subdued, she pulls it through the sheet, wraps it in silk, unless it is very small, and then commences to eat it.

The most easily observed of the common garden money spiders is *Linyphia triangularis*, whose predominantly black, white and brown females reach just over 6mm in length. You will find this species hanging beneath the hammock of her web built in bushes or other robust plants as well as in small trees, often fairly high up. Its very wide distribution excludes just the Outer Hebrides, the very north of Scotland and the Northern Isles.

Many other species of money spider can also turn up in the garden but are less easily identified. Suffice it to say that any tiny black or dark grey spider, seemingly appearing out of nowhere, will be a money spider. In terms of numbers, they are among the most numerous of spiders. In some years in short, open grassland their numbers can reach 5.5million per hectare, (2.25million per acre). You can get some idea of their numbers by going out early on a dewy morning in late summer and looking at your lawn. All of those tiny, dew-covered webs, not much bigger than a 50p piece, are the handiwork of the tiny money spiders that live there.

Linyphia triangularis Common hammock spider (Linyphiidae) female feeding on a parent bug *Elasmucha grisea*

Linyphia (=nereine) peltata Foliage hammock spider (Linyphiidae) female on the edge of her web

Commonly asked questions about spiders 11

DO ANY BRITISH SPIDERS BITE HUMANS?

This question really needs asking in two different ways. Do any British spiders bite humans as part of their day to day activities? The answer to this is an emphatic no!! We are far to big to be considered as possible prey by any spider. Do any British spiders bite humans by accident or when mishandled? The answer to this is yes. Compared to us spiders, are tiny and if you pick one of the larger ones up clumsily it will probably attempt to stick its fangs into you in self-defence. You may feel a tiny pricking as it does so but none of our spiders can do you any harm. Spiders that are known to bite in this way are the sheet web spiders, *Tegenaria* species and also the woodlouse spider, which, of course, has huge jaws.

WHY DON'T SPIDERS GET STUCK IN THEIR OWN WEBS?

Not all of the silk used in making a catching web is sticky and some webs are not sticky at all. The best examples here are the webs of orb-weaving spiders. These familiar objects consist of a series of radial spokes attached to a set of scaffolding lines, none of which are sticky. On to these, the spider then lays a very long spiral of sticky threads. When a flying insect collides with the web, it inevitably contacts some of this sticky silk and becomes trapped. The spider knows of this sticky silk and when moving around on the web walks only on the non-sticky silk. Occasionally, a spider may accidentally come into contact with its own sticky silk and then it becomes trapped just like any helpless insect.

HOW DO SPIDERS DEAL WITH LARGE, STINGING INSECTS SUCH AS WASPS AND BEES?

Both web-builders and free-living hunting spiders come across dangerous insects at one time or another. The web-builders have a choice as to what to do if, say, a wasp ends up in the web. They can either cut it out or, if the spider is a large one, she can immobilise it by throwing silk over it, carefully avoiding the sting. Once it is bound up, she can then feed on it like any other insect. The common flower spider often kills bees, including large bumble bees, and occasionally even wasps. She uses stealth. As the insect lands beside her, she quietly bites it in the leg, her poison acting so fast that it has no time to retaliate. The little red-and-white and white cobweb spider uses the same technique to immobilise a bumble bee many times her size.

WHY DO YOU OFTEN FIND A WEB FULL OF TINY FLIES, WHICH THE OWNER DOES NOT SEEM TO BOTHER TO EAT?

There are probably two answers to this, either or both being true. Firstly, small insects falling into a web struggle so gently that the spider is unable to detect their presence, as it normally would for a larger insect. The second possibility is that the spider detects the insect and then appraises it size, either by the strength of its struggles or by checking its size by direct contact. If it 'feels' that it is too small to make a meal, it just leaves it.

WHERE DO OUR GARDEN-DWELLING SPIDERS SPEND THE WINTER?

Spiders overwinter in a number of different ways. Some, either as adults or immatures, choose a suitable site which is well protected from the harsh conditions of winter, and remain there until the following spring. Some species of *Tegenaria*, which, of course, include the house spiders, come indoors during the winter and, as a result, some individuals may live for as long as 2 or 3 years.

Alternatively, many other species overwinter as eggs, the adults of the year all dying by the time the cold days of winter arrive. The eggs hatch the following spring and the spiderlings then have to feed and grow to egg-laying size before the autumn comes round again and they reach the end of their brief lives.

SPIDERS DON'T HAVE WINGS, SO HOW DO THEY GET AROUND FROM PLACE TO PLACE?

One obvious way that they can and do get around is to walk. The house spiders that spend the summer outside make their way 'on foot' to our houses, probably scuttling in without being noticed when we open the front or back door at night. Most baby spiders and many of the money spiders use an alternative method, they 'balloon'. They usually do this when there is a light wind blowing. First of all they climb up to a fairly high point, such as the tip of a grass stem or the top of a fence post. They then face into the wind, stand high on their legs, raise the tip of the abdomen as high as they can and release a stream of silk. The breeze lifts the silk high up above them and, we assume that, as soon as they feel sufficient pull on the line they let go and are lifted gently up into the air. They may then be carried a few metres, a few hundreds of metres, a few kilometres or even hundreds or thousands of kilometres. This can happen when they are carried thousands of metres up into the jetstreams. Sampling nets carried on aircraft find these tiny aeronauts still alive at these great heights and, assuming that they land safely in a suitable habitat, they can take up residence there. The money spiders are the greatest of the aeronauts as adults and this probably accounts for the wide distribution of many species around the whole of the northern hemisphere.

FURTHER READING

Preston-Mafham, R. & Preston-Mafham, K., 1984. *Spiders of the World.* Blandford Press, 192pp. (An introduction to the biology and natural history of the major spider families of the world).

Preston-Mafham, K. & Preston-Mafham, R., 1996. *The Natural History of Spiders* Crowood Press, 160pp (An easy to read, well-illustrated introduction to the biology and natural history of spiders).

Preston-Mafham, K., 1998. *Apple Identifier – Spiders* Apple Press, 80pp. (An illustrated identifier for 90 of the world's spiders).

Roberts, Michael. J., 1995. *Spiders of Britain & Northern Europe* HarperCollins Publishers, 384pp. (A very good field guide to start you on the road to identifying the spiders that you find. Includes 450 of the 600 or so species found in the British Isles).

Jones, R., 1989. *The Country Life Guide to Spiders of Britain & Northern Europe* Hamlyn, 320pp. (A very good photographic guide to use alongside Roberts but you will have to look for a secondhand copy).

USEFUL WEBSITES

Images and descriptions of 220 species of spider common in NW Europe at www.xs4all.nl/~ednieuw/Spiders/spidhome.html

The arachnological hub of the worldwide web, for spiders, scorpions etc. at www.arachnology.org/